MY SPECIAL BOOK OF

Children's Verses

Marshall Cavendish

CONTENTS

THE SONG OF THE ENGINE

With snort and pant the engine dragged
    Its heavy train uphill,
And puffed these words the while she puffed
    And laboured with a will:

"I think — I can — I think — I can,
    I've got — to reach — the top,
I'm sure — I can — I will — get there,
    I sim — ply must — not stop!"

At last the top was reached and passed,
    And then — how changed the song!
The wheels all joined in the engine's joy,
    As quickly she tore along!

"I knew I could do it, I knew I could win,
    Oh, rickety rackety rack!
And now for a roaring rushing race
    On my smooth and shining track!"

FATHER WILLIAM

"You are old, Father William," the young man said,
  "And your hair has become very white;
And yet you incessantly stand on your head —
  Do you think, at your age, it is right?"

"In my youth," Father William replied to his son,
  "I feared it might injure the brain;
But now that I'm perfectly sure I have none,
  Why, I do it again and again."

"You are old," said the youth, "as I mentioned before,
  And have grown most uncommonly fat;
Yet you turned a back somersault in at the door —
  Pray, what is the reason of that?"

"In my youth," said the sage, as he shook his grey locks
  "I kept all my limbs very supple
By the use of this ointment — one shilling the box —
  Allow me to sell you a couple?"

"You are old," said the youth, "and your jaws are too weak
    For anything rougher than suet;
Yet you finished the goose, with the bones and the beak —
    Pray, how did you manage to do it?"

"In my youth," said his father, "I took to the law,
    And argued each case with my wife;
And the muscular strength which it gave my jaw,
    Has lasted the rest of my life."

"You are old," said the youth, "one would hardly suppose
    That your eye was as steady as ever;
Yet you balance an eel on the end of your nose —
    What made you so awfully clever?"

"I have answered three questions, and that is enough,"
    Said his father. "Don't give yourself airs!
Do you think I can listen all day to such stuff!
    Be off, or I'll kick you downstairs!"

THE COTTAGE

When I live in a Cottage
I shall keep in my Cottage

Two different Dogs,
Three creamy Cows,
Four giddy Goats,
Five Pewter Pots
Six silver Spoons
Seven busy Beehives
Eight ancient Appletrees
Nine red Rosebushes
Ten teeming Teapots
Eleven chirping Chickens
Twelve cosy Cats with their Kittenish Kittens and
One blessed Baby in a Basket.

That's what I'll have when I live in my Cottage.

My UNCLE PAUL of PIMLICO

My Uncle Paul of Pimlico
Has seven cats as white as snow,
Who sit at his enormous feet
And watch him, as a special treat,
Play the piano upside-down,
In his delightful dressing-gown;
The firelight leaps, the parlour glows,
And, while the music ebbs and flows,
They smile (while purring the refrains),
At little thoughts that cross their brains.

O here it is and there it is...

O here it is! and there it is!
And no-one knows
                    whose share it is,
Nor dares to stake a claim.
But we have seen it in the air,
A fairy, like a William pear—
With but itself to blame.

A thug it is! and smug it is;
And like a floating pug it is,
Above the orchard trees.
It has no right—no right at all
To soar above the orchard wall,
                    With chilblains on its knees.

Goblin Market

Morning and evening,
Maids heard the goblins cry:
"Come buy our orchard fruits,
Come buy, come buy:
Apples and quinces,
Lemons and oranges,
Plump unpecked cherries,
Melons and raspberries,
Bloom-down-cheeked peaches.
Swart-headed mulberries,
Wild free-born cranberries,
Crab-apples, dewberries,
Pine-apples, blackberries,
Apricots, strawberries; —
All ripe together
In summer weather —
Morns that pass by,
Fair eaves that fly;
Come buy, come buy:
Our grapes fresh from the vine,
Pomegranates full and fine,
Dates and sharp bullaces,
Rare peaches and greengages,
Damsons and bilberries,
Taste them and try:
Currants and gooseberries,
Bright fire-like barberries,
Figs to fill your mouth,
Citrons from the South,
Sweet to tongue and sound to eye;
Come buy, come buy."

The HUMAN FLY from BENDIGO

My favourite uncle, Tim McFife,
Was very keen on circus life.
He had an act which stole the show
'The Human Fly from Bendigo'.

Each night, he showed his expertise
And balanced on the high trapeze
Then, spreading both his silver wings,
He fluttered round the Roman rings.

As spotlights blazed on Uncle Tim,
A thousand eyes were fixed on him,
A phantom flying to and fro —
'The Human Fly from Bendigo'.

And so he stunned them every night,
Dressed up in foil and party lights,
Suspended by a handy wire
To keep him flying even higher.

One dreadful night, the wire went slack
And Uncle landed on his back
But, ever faithful to his pride,
He kicked his legs, buzzed once, then died.

ALDRED.

12

THE MARROG

My desk's at the back of the class
   And nobody, nobody knows
   I'm a Marrog from Mars
With a body of brass
   And seventeen fingers and toes.

Wouldn't they shriek if they knew
   I've three eyes at the back of my head
   And my hair is bright purple
My nose is deep blue
   And my teeth are half yellow, half-red.

My five arms are silver, and spiked
   With knives on them sharper than spears.
I could go back right now if I liked —
   And return in a million light-years.

I could gobble them all
For I'm seven foot tall
   And I'm breathing green flames from my ears.

Wouldn't they yell if they knew,
   If they guessed that a Marrog was here?
Ha-ha, they haven't a clue —
   Or wouldn't they tremble with fear!
"Look, look, a Marrog"
   They'd all scream — and SMACK
The blackboard would fall and the ceiling would crack
   And teacher would faint, I suppose.
But I grin to myself, sitting right at the back
   And nobody, nobody knows.

13

Rilloby-rill

Grasshoppers four a-fiddling went,
  Heigh-ho! never be still!
They earned but little towards their rent
But all day long with their elbows bent
  They fiddled a tune called Rilloby-rilloby,
  Fiddled a tune called Rilloby-rill.

Grasshoppers soon on fairies came,
  Heigh-ho! never be still!
Fairies asked with a manner of blame,
  "Where do you come from, what is your name,
  What do you want with your Rilloby-rilloby,
  What do you want with your Rilloby-rill?"

"Madam, you see before you stand,
  Heigh-ho! never be still!
The Old Original Favourite Grand
Grasshoppers' Green Herbarian Band,
  And the tune we play is Rilloby-rilloby,
  Madam, the tune is Rilloby-rill."

Windy Nights

Whenever the moon and stars are set,
  Whenever the wind is high,
All night long in the dark and wet,
  A man goes riding by.
Late in the night when the fires are out,
Why does he gallop and gallop about?

Whenever the trees are crying aloud,
  And ships are tossed at sea,
By, on the highway, low and loud,
  By at the gallop goes he.
By at the gallop he goes, and then
By he comes back at the gallop again.

SHEEP DOG

Born one day in a field of sheep,
Shaggy and grey and confused with sleep —
The one his mother didn't keep —
Bruno.

Wagging, bounding, panting, grinning:
He thought himself from the beginning
The one and only sheep to sing in
Tune-o.

For when the moon was full and bright
He'd creep away through stark moonlight
And howl and growl and bark all night
Through-o.

But then one night, as Bruno sang,
The shiny Dog Star bared its fangs
And, joining in, it sang along —
A duo.

"Two dogs we are and dogs agree
That sheep, however fine they be,
Could never bleat as sweet as we
Two do-o!"

Rhubarb Ted

I knew a funny little man
His name was Rhubarb Ted;
They called him that because he wore
Rhubarb on his head.

I'd grown so used to this strange sight,
The cause I did not seek;
But then one day to my surprise,
I saw he wore a leek.

I asked him if he'd please explain,
And let me know the reason;
He said, 'I'm wearing leek because
Rhubarb's out of season!'

THERE ONCE WAS A PUFFIN

Oh, there once was a Puffin
Just the shape of a muffin,
And he lived on an island
In the bright blue sea!

He ate little fishes,
That were most delicious,
And he had them for supper
And he had them for tea.

But this poor little Puffin,
He couldn't play nothin',
For he hadn't anybody
To play with at all.

So he sat on his island,
And he cried for a while, and
He felt very lonely,
And he felt very small.

Then along came the fishes,
And they said, "If you wishes,
You can have us for playmates,
Instead of for tea!"

So they now play together,
In all sorts of weather,
And the Puffin eats pancakes,
Like you and like me.

Upon My Golden Backbone

Upon my golden backbone
I float like any cork,
That hasn't yet been washed ashore
Or swallowed by a shark.

I never seem to want to snarl
In jungles all day long —
I've been so much upon my back
My legs aren't very strong.

It's all because a Pelican
I *didn't* eat one day,
Decided to look after me
That I behave this way.

And so, while Other Tigers slink
From tree . . . to tree . . . to tree,
I lie upon my back, and blink,
In Aqueous Ecstasy.

IF YOU SHOULD MEET A CROCODILE

If you should meet a crocodile,
Don't take a stick and poke him;
Ignore the welcome in his smile,
Be careful not to stroke him.
For as he sleeps upon the Nile,
He thinner gets and thinner;
And whene'er you meet a crocodile
He's ready for his dinner.

The SUNLIGHT falls upon the GRASS

The sunlight falls upon the grass;
It falls upon the tower;
Upon my spectacles of brass
It falls with all its power.

It falls on everything it can,
For that is how it's made;
And it would fall on me, except,
That I am in the shade.

A Child's Thought

At seven, when I go to bed,
I find such pictures in my head:
Castles with dragons prowling round,
Gardens where magic fruits are found;
Fair ladies prisoned in a tower,
Or lost in an enchanted bower;
While gallant horsemen ride by streams
That border all this land of dreams
I find, so clearly in my head
At seven, when I go to bed.

At seven, when I wake again,
The magic land I seek in vain;
A chair stands where the castle frowned,
The carpet hides the garden ground,
No fairies trip across the floor,
Boots, and not horsemen, flank the door,
And where the blue streams rippling ran
Is now a bath and water-can;
I seek the magic land in vain
At seven, when I wake again.